The Fantastic Four at Frog Farm

Wes Magee
Illustrated by Amanda Wood

OXFORD
UNIVERSITY PRESS

Rachel and Richard,
Paul from next door,
and Rover the dog
are The Fantastic Four.

It was breezy and bright
in the middle of May
when they went on a trip
to Frog Farm for the day.

Frog Farm is a wonderful
place to explore.
It's just the right place
for The Fantastic Four.

Rachel and Richard
saw a lamb and a hen.
Paul was licked
by a calf in its pen.

Rover and Mum
went too near the goat.
It chased the dog
and chewed Mum's red coat.

Rachel saw two chicks
out of the pen.
Gently she gave them
back to the hen.

Frog Farm is a wonderful
place to explore.
It's just the right place
for The Fantastic Four.

The Fantastic Four
had a ride on a train.
It went round Frog Farm.
Then it went round again.

The train rattled on.
Its whistle went peep.
"Look there," shouted Paul,
"some cows and some sheep!"

Frog Farm is a wonderful
place to explore.
It's just the right place
for The Fantastic Four.

They got off the train.
Mum said, “Time for lunch.”
All you could hear
was munch-ity-munch.

Then in the playground
The Four climbed a wall.
They swung on a rope.
Mum said, "Don't you fall!"

"Bouncy Castle! Come on!"
They bounced up and down,
and Richard said, "Hey,
I can roll like a clown."

Frog Farm is a wonderful
place to explore.
It's just the right place
for The Fantastic Four.

“Ponies, Mum, ponies!”
Richard called out.
“Don’t be so noisy.
They’ll run if you shout.”

Rachel rode Meg.
Richard rode Mog.
Paul rode big Ginger
and Mum held the dog.

The three ponies trotted
and jumped over logs.
They went to the pond
and saw millions of frogs!

The ponies were thirsty.
They bent down to get
a nice drink of water,
and Richard got wet.

Richard went under
and came up for air.
"Oh, no!" shouted Mum,
"There's a frog in your hair!"

After the laughter,
the barks and the screams,
The Fantastic Four
tucked into ice-creams.

It was time to go home.
Mum said, “It’s getting late.”
“I love it at Frog Farm,”
said Rachel. “It’s great.”

Frog Farm is a wonderful
place to explore.
It's just the right place
for The Fantastic Four.